Turquoise
Ruby
Pink Diamond
Black Opal
Emerald
Pearl Necklace
(Russian setting)

ACKNOWLEDGEMENTS: *p. 9, Academia, Venice: Art Reference Bureau; p. 14, Metropolitan Museum of Art; p. 16 upper right, Metropolitan Museum of Art: Pulitzer Fund, 1942; p. 22, De Beers Consolidated Mines, Ltd.; p. 29, Metropolitan Museum of Art: Dick Fund, 1926; p. 42, Woburn Abbey, Bedfordshire, England*

PUBLISHED BY
PAUL HAMLYN LIMITED • Westbook House • Fulham Broadway • London

PRINTED IN THE U.S.A.

GEMS AND JEWELLERY

WRITTEN AND ILLUSTRATED

BY NED SEIDLER

PAUL HAMLYN • LONDON

PUT A SNAKE in a jar with a sapphire and the viper will instantly die. ■ Hold a moonstone in your mouth and it will refresh your memory. ■ Drink wine from an amethyst cup and you will never get drunk. (The Greek word *amethyst* means "not to intoxicate".) ■ Beliefs like these kept the ancient lapidaries (*lapis* is Latin for "stone") busy filling the demand for a wide variety of charmstones. ■ Today, scientists know a great deal more about gems. They know, for instance, how they were formed. Billions of years ago, when the molten earth began to solidify, the outside layers cooled relatively quickly to form the fine-grained rocks of which most of the world is composed. But the

A busy lapidary shop depicted in a medieval woodcut

deeper layers cooled more slowly, and there formed the crystal-minerals we know today as gemstones. ■ The ancients knew none of this, and, as with all things they did not understand, they made up stories to explain the origin of the beautiful "buds" which they found (in Latin *gemma* means "bud"). ■ Sapphire, according to oriental legend, was a drop of *Amrita,* a drink of the gods which conferred immortality. The gods allowed it to solidify so that mortals could get a glimpse of Nirvana. ■ Rubies, it was believed, grew like plants and ripened. If a ruby was not the prized deep red colour, it was thought to have been "picked" too soon. ■ The ancients not only invented stories to explain the origin of gems, but they endowed them with strange and magical powers. Many gems were believed to warn their owners of impending danger by changing their colour. King John of England wore a turquoise to detect poison. Mary, Queen of Scots, used a diamond for this same purpose. ■ The colour of a stone often suggested its therapeutic use. Bloodstones, believed to have been formed when drops of Christ's blood fell on jasper at the foot of the cross, were assigned many magical powers. Writing in the fifteenth century, the Renaissance painter-historian Giorgio Vasari tells of being stricken with a hemorrhage in the presence of a fellow painter, Luca Signorelli. Si-

gnorelli applied a bloodstone to the back of Vasari's neck and the flow of blood was immediately staunched. ■ The use of gems to bring good luck far antedates recorded history. Gemstones have been found on prehistoric monuments, in the tombs of the Pharaohs and of the Incas. ■ And, of course, they are worn to this day as birthstones, the Greeks having been largely responsible for expanding the influence of astrology to include gemstones. The wearing of birthstones, as we know the custom, probably began in the eighteenth century, but its origins date to ancient history. The book of Exodus describes the twelve stones of the high priest's breastplate. The first row contained sard, topaz, and carbuncle; the second, emerald, sapphire, and diamond; the third, ligure, agate, amethyst; and the fourth, beryl, onyx, and jasper. Only ligure has never been identified. Several of the stones, however, are probably not the gems which we describe by these names today. Diamond, for example, could not be cut and polished until the fifteenth century, and so it is likely that

"The price of amber enclosing a small figure exceeds that of a healthy slave," said Pliny. Medieval wood cut shows tree oozing amber sap

the high priest's "diamond" was what we call rock crystal. His "sapphire" was almost surely lapis lazuli; "jasper", probably carnelian; "carbuncle", garnet; and "beryl", peridot. ■ Amber was probably the earliest of the gems used for personal adornment. The ancients believed it to be the rays of the setting sun, solidified by the cool waters of the sea. It is one of the few gems which are not an inorganic crystal. It is, rather, the vegetable kingdom's contribution to the world of gems—the fossilized gum of extinct coniferous trees. As the viscous fluid oozed from these ancient trees, insects and plants were caught and entombed forever. Of amber, Pope wrote: *Pretty in amber to observe the forms/Of hairs or straws or dirt or grubs or worms/The things we know are neither rich nor rare/But wonder how the devil they got there.* ■ Nature with

Detail from The Presentation of the Virgin *by Titian shows gems on priest's breastplate*

a
c
d
b
e

her infinite treasure of oddities produces minerals whose crystal structure yields ready-made charms. Staurolite, a stone of twin crystals at right angles, presents the shape of a cross. According to legend, when the fairies wept at being told of the crucifixion of Christ, their tear drops crystallized into the form of a cross as they fell. To this day they are called fairy stones, and Theodore Roosevelt is said to have worn one as a watch fob. Chiastolite is another oddity. During the growth of the crystal, carbonaceous matter arranges itself in a regular pattern. When cut into slices, a black cross on a yellow background is seen. Polished slices are mounted and worn as charms. ■ Occasionally, there is a basis in fact for the power attributed to a gemstone. Gazing at a crystal ball will not unveil the future. But prolonged staring at its refracted light will tire the optic nerve, and images from the mind of the fatigued viewer will seem to emanate from the ball. ■ Men first used gems as decorations and talismen to court the favour of the gods and to ward off evil. As civilization progressed and men began to own an increasing number of personal possessions, the need arose for the legal documentation of these possessions. Gemstone beads, now taking the form of cylinders, were incised with personalized carvings and were used as seals of ownership. Engraved gemstone cylinders probably originated 5,000 years ago in Mesopotamia. ■ Seals of Babylonia and Assyria, dating from 4,000 to 3,000 B.C., have come down to us, preserving a rare record of those prehistoric civilizations. The seals often took the forms of

Fifteenth century print (a) showing the "curing" of a nosebleed with a bloodstone (b). Pocket-sized eighteenth-century quartz crystal ball (c) "foretold" future. Twinned staurolite crystals (d) and chiastolite (e) are nature's ready-made charms

deities or animals of combat. Sometimes, however, they were more personal. The seals of doctors, for example, revealed the owner's name and the scalpel and lancet of his trade. ■ Deeds of sale were accompanied by the seal of the seller. Marriage contracts required the seal of both parties. Debts were acknowledged with the seal of the debtor, and the clay tablet certifying the debt was destroyed when the obligation had been discharged. ■ The cylinder seals, worn on a string about the wrists or neck, were decorative as well as practical, and a man's importance could be judged by the number of seals he wore. ■ The ancient Egyptians adopted the Mesopotamian cylinders and later refined them into rings in the shape of scarabs,

Impression of an Assyrian lapis lazuli cylinder rolled on unhardened clay. Many gemstones, like green amazon stone and orange agate, were skilfully carved for use as seals of ownership

horned beetles sacred to the Egyptians. The top of the ring was carved to resemble the scarab, while the underside was incised in a personal design. When the ring was off the finger, it could be reversed and the under side used as a seal. Parenthetically, it should be noted that seals made forgery easy. Jezebel used her husband's signet ring to sign a false letter. ■ The ancient Egyptians gave us not only the signet ring, but a tradition that has far outlived the use of rings as seals. The Egyptian husband placed a ring on his wife's finger as a sign that he trusted her with the custody of his household and possessions, and from this custom came our wedding rings. ■ It was the Greek craftsmen who brought the art of gem cutting to its pinnacle of excellence, giving ancient sculpture its perfect counterpart in miniature gem engravings. Some were engraved with only the aid of a sapphire point. But most required a

Egyptian wall painting shows lapidaries at work. They are depicted carrying jewellery, weighing gems and even hiding a tray of gems under a tablecloth (shown between the heads of the two figures at lower right) to protect it from thieves

technique that was evolved about 5,000 years ago and is still used in modified form today. Drills of various shapes were attached to a manually operated wheel. The actual cutting was done by emery powder between the drill and the stone. ■ The ancients polished gems in rounded cabochon forms, the art of faceting being unknown. Louis de Berquen of Bruges first used the accurate facet cut about 1476. Hindu lapidaries had long known that a diamond could be polished by rubbing it against another diamond. What Berquen discovered was that this process yielded a dust which could cut diamonds with great precision. The rosette cut, developed soon afterwards, prevailed until a 17th-century Venetian evolved the brilliant cut. Most minerals from which gems are cut are found in crystal form. They may be individual crystals or aggregates. Nature presents them in orderly and consistent form. A

The art of the ancient Egyptian lapidaries reached its peak in this magnificent gold necklace inlaid with semi-precious stones. It was worn by Princess Sit Hat-Hor Yunet of the XII dynasty some 3,700 years ago. Now in the Metropolitan Museum in New York, it is considered the finest piece of Egyptian jewellery extant. The chain is composed of gold, red carnelian, turquoise, and lapis lazuli. In the wings of the hawks, alternating inlays of turquoise and lapis lazuli delineate the feathers. The Egyptians made their seals in the form of the sacred scarab

Red carnelian scarab, executed in the sixth century B.C. by Greek craftsmen. Life-sized, above, its impression is enlarged at right to show how well the classical elegance of Greek sculpture was achieved in the delicate incisings

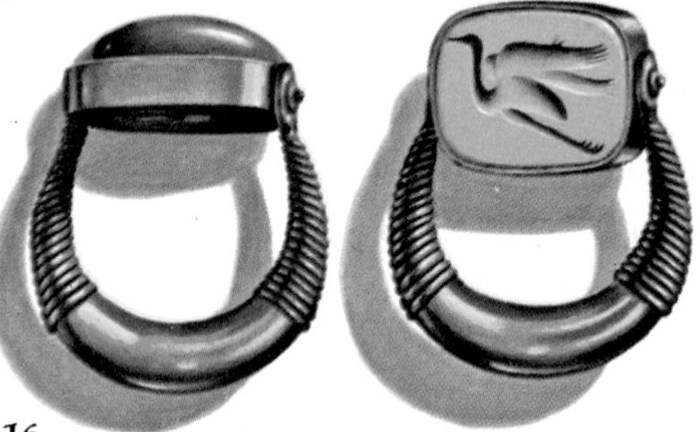

Mounted in swivel rings, engraved stones could be worn decoratively as a cabochon cut, left, *or, reversed, they could be used for seals,* right. *Using a variety of gems, engravers covered wide range of subjects*

garnet found in Ceylon is identical with one from Virginia. ■ Of the many minerals found on earth, only a few qualify as gemstones. ■ Of these, only four qualify for the noble title of "precious". They are the diamond, emerald, sapphire, and ruby. They have earned their title by exhibiting to superb degree the qualities of rarity, beauty, colour, and hardness. ■ A gem's hardness is rated in terms of what minerals can scratch it. The harder the mineral, the higher it stands in the Mohs scale, named after a Viennese mineralogist. Diamond, the hardest natural substance known to man, is rated #10 and is followed by corundum, #9, from which we obtain rubies and sapphires. The difference between diamond and corundum

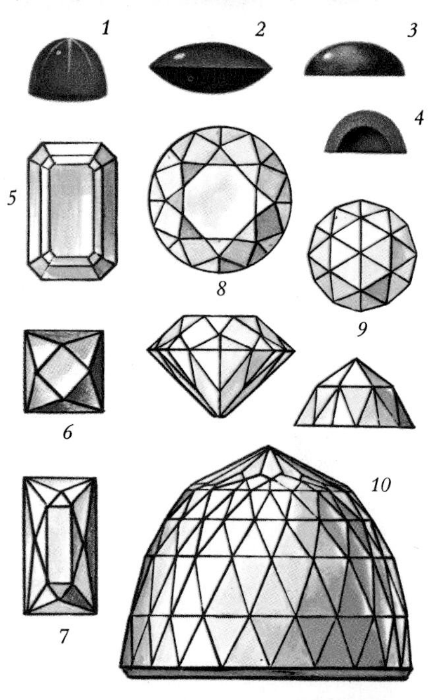

TYPES OF CUTTING. *The first four are cabochon styles: 1. High. 2. Lentil. 3. Single. 4. Hollow (shown in cross-section). 5. Emerald or step cut. 6. French cut. 7. Scissor cut. 8. Circular brilliant. 9. Old rose cut. 10. Great Mogul diamond, in multiple rose cut*

Golden beryl

Rose beryl *Goshenite* *Blue beryl*

Aquamarine in natural state

Emerald in natural state

The mineral beryl yields all the gems shown here. Aquamarine ranges in colour from bluish green to sea green. Colour variations are caused by minute traces of impurities. A trace of chromium accounts for the deep green of emerald. Rose beryl is also called morganite after J. P. Morgan, noted financier

is greater than the difference between corundum and talc, the softest mineral of the scale. Quartz is #7 on the Mohs scale. Because of the abrasive action of the many particles of quartz dust present in the air, gems to be mounted in rings should rank higher than #7. All precious stones do. ■ Beryl is an example of one crystal mineral yielding several gemstones, each of distinct colour and name. ■ A single diamond (from the Greek *adamas*, meaning "invincible") may be worth thousands of pounds. Yet it is only a cousin of coal—carbon trapped in molten lava and transformed under immense heat and pressure into a king's ransom. ■ Diamonds were first found in India. In the mid-1600s the French jeweller Tavernier brought back to France fabulous tales of India's diamonds. Each of India's largest diamonds had its own bloody and villainous history. Tavernier himself brought back a huge blue diamond and sold it to Louis XIV. Stolen during the French Revolution, it is believed to have turned up as the famed Hope Diamond, harbinger of ill fate. The Orloff, stolen from an idol's eye in a Brahmin temple, eventually became part of Russia's crown

Most gemstones are cut from well-formed crystals or aggregates like smoky quartz. Exceptions include agate, composed of microscopic crystals; and opal, an amorphous silica which shows no crystal structure.

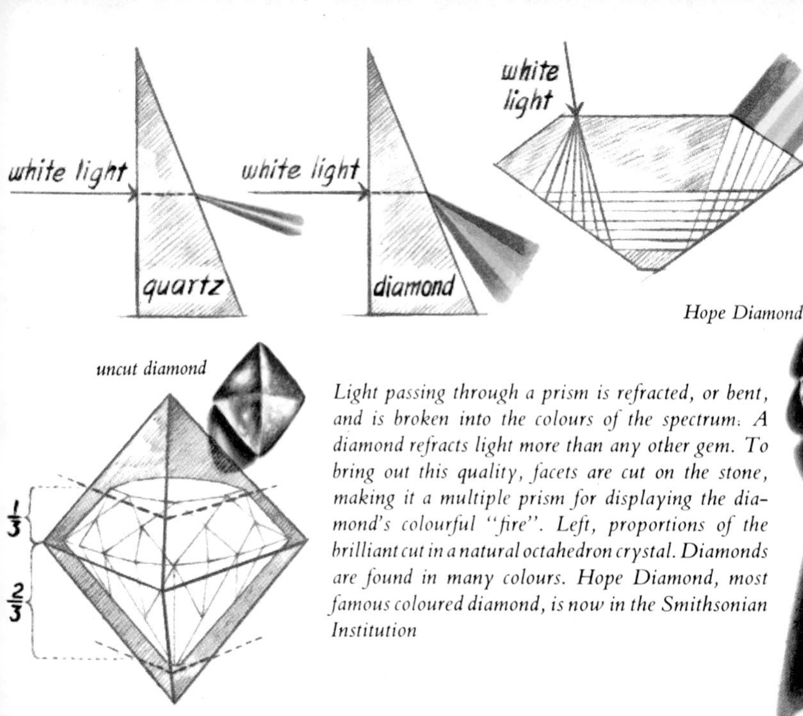

Hope Diamond

Light passing through a prism is refracted, or bent, and is broken into the colours of the spectrum. A diamond refracts light more than any other gem. To bring out this quality, facets are cut on the stone, making it a multiple prism for displaying the diamond's colourful "fire". Left, proportions of the brilliant cut in a natural octahedron crystal. Diamonds are found in many colours. Hope Diamond, most famous coloured diamond, is now in the Smithsonian Institution

Grain marked in Indian ink

*teel blade is inserted
n marked groove and
iamond is split with
ingle blow of mallet*

jewels. It is thought to have originally been part of the Great Mogul, largest known Indian stone, which has been missing for many years. Other famous Indian stones are the Koh-i-noor ("mountain of light") and the Regent, once Napoleon's, now in the Louvre. ■ The discovery in 1867 of a small shiny pebble on the banks of the Orange River in South Africa foreshadowed the discovery on the De Beers farm of the most fabulous diamond mine in history: the Kimberley, site of an extinct volcano. In a short time 1,500 claimants were furiously digging in an elliptical area less than a quarter of a mile wide. Prices of claims jumped from £180 to £7,000 in a matter of months. ■ In the hurried excavation, the sides of the mine frequently collapsed and many lives were lost. With increasing mining difficulties, amalgamations became desirable, and control of the Kimberley eventually passed into the hands of two men, Barney Barnato and Cecil Rhodes. In 1889, after a lengthy struggle of forces, Rhodes, backed by the House of Rothschild, bought out Barnato with a single historic cheque for £5,338,650, then worth about £9,000,000. So was formed De Beers Consolidated Mines, Ltd. Later, rich diamond deposits

The mouth of the Kimberley mine shortly after discovery. Hundreds of strings mark claims

were found elsewhere, particularly in the Belgian Congo. Largely through the efforts of De Beers, the Diamond Trading Company, Ltd. was established to control the world market in diamonds and so maintain their price. Today about 95% of all the world's production is bought by the company for resale. When a new lot is to be sold, dealers throughout the world are invited to attend a "sight" of the new stones. In his application the dealer must indicate how much he intends to spend. If his application is accepted, he sends a representative to the Diamond Trading Company's London office. There, seated at a table by the north light, the prospective purchaser may examine the stones for sale. The company sells them in lots, and if a dealer wants to buy any stones at all, he must buy the entire lot. ■ It was at another South African mine, the Premier, that the world's largest diamond, the Cullinan, was discovered in 1905. Weighing

The Kimberley today. Open pit mining was abandoned in 1899. Vertical shaft goes down 3,600 feet. Every 40 feet, horizontal tunnels are bored to volcanic pipe. Blue ground is drawn from the side of the mine farthest from means of access and taken to surface in huge buckets. Top levels are successively set back and waste rock falls into the gap

an incredible 3106 carats (over 1½ pounds), it was more than three times the size of any diamond ever known. Yet close examination revealed it to be only part of a larger stone, never found. ■ When the Transvaal government presented it to King Edward VII, he was so unimpressed by its raw appearance that he declared, "I should have kicked it aside as a lump of glass if I had seen it in the road". A flaw in the centre necessitated cleaving the stone. Despite its hardness, a miscalculated blow could have shattered the diamond, and with it a fortune. The renowned Dutch gem cutter Asscher, after months of study, struck

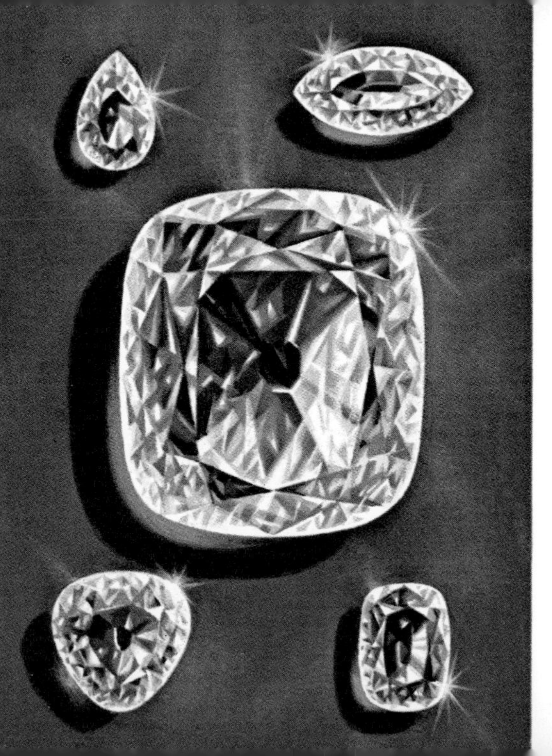

the critical blow. The steel blade broke, but the diamond remained whole. Later, on a second try, he split the diamond perfectly, and fainted dead away. ■ Today the four largest stones from the Cullinan, known as the "Stars of Africa", are part of England's crown jewels. The two largest are, respectively, in the British royal sceptre and Imperial State Crown. The two others are both in the Queen's State Crown. ■ As they come from the mines, very few diamonds are of gem quality, but none are wasted. They can cut, grind, and saw

Nine major stones shown here approximately life size were cut from the Cullinan, far left. *Pear-shaped Cullinan I, 530 carats; square-brilliant Cullinan II, 317 carats; pear-shaped Culliman III, 95 carats; square-brilliant Cullinan IV, 63 carats. The other five shown here weigh from almost 19 carats to about 4.4. In addition, 96 lesser gems were cut and many unpolished fragments were found suitable for industrial use*

today's tough metal alloys efficiently. In the teeth of a drill, they can bore through solid rock. They are also used as dies and gramophone needles. Together with the diamond, the ruby, the sapphire, and the emerald make up the royal foursome of precious stones. Varieties of these three gems are shown life-size at left. The emerald is set in a classic Russian diamond brooch. It is unusually large; emeralds of this size hardly ever reach the open market. They are snapped up by members of the inner circle of wealthy collectors. The hexagonal crystal is a specimen of emerald as it is found in its natural form. In earlier times, crystals such as this were often cut in slices, which were polished and worn as personal adornment. ▪ All the other stones in the illustration are rubies or sapphires; they are varieties of the same mineral—corundum. The deep red stones are rubies; the rest are sapphires. While cornflower blue is traditionally associated with sapphires, they come in a wide range of colours. Corundum also belongs to the hexagonal crystal system, and is often found in the slender shapes shown at centre. The colour frequently lies in uneven bands, and only by expert cutting will the deepest colour dominate the gem. ▪ The 563-carat Star of India sapphire, the world's largest, and the 100-carat De Long ruby are no longer in the hands of private collectors. They can now be

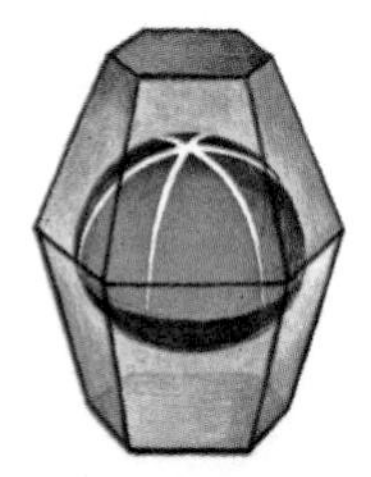

This schematic drawing shows the proper orientation for cutting a star sapphire. To display asterism, the stone must be cut on the vertical axis of the crystal. Asterism is found only in crystals of a cloudy appearance. Occasionally, two or more stones can be cut on the axis of the same crystal.

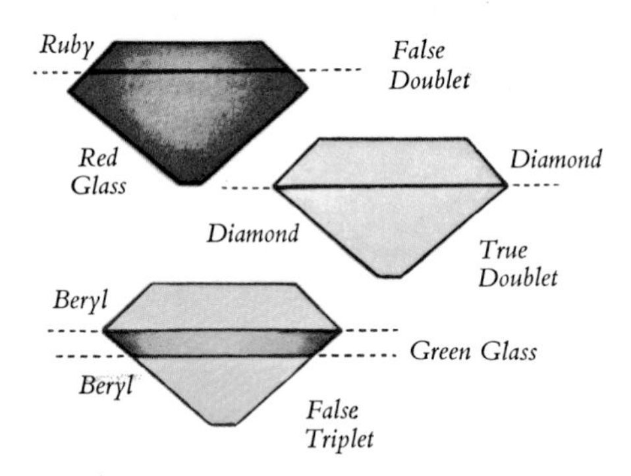

Gems are not always of one piece; doublets and triplets are thin slices of gemstones joined together. True doublets and triplets are stones of one kind cemented together, with the seam often hidden by the setting. False doublets have a genuine crown and underparts of glass or inferior stone. The false triplet shown here sandwiches a slice of deep green glass between pale beryl for emerald-like effect

seen at the Museum of Natural History in New York. ■ Like emeralds, pure red rubies of more than ten carats are extremely rare and enormously valuable. The most highly esteemed specimens of pigeon-blood red come from Burma. Over the centuries, Ceylon, India, and Thailand have also yielded fine stones, but the extraordinarily beautiful orange sapphire known as the Paparadscha—shown in background, partly hidden by curtain—can be found only in Ceylon. ■ Priceless though diamonds are, a large emerald without a flaw is so rare that carat for carat it is apt to be worth more than a fine diamond. Legend says that when Satan fell from Heaven, a single emerald dropped from his crown. From this stone was fashioned the Holy Grail, from which Christ drank at the Last Supper. The Knights of the Round Table swore to find the Grail, and Wagner's opera *Parsifal* tells the story of the search. ■ The name "emerald" comes from the Persian *zummurrund*, meaning "green". When Pizarro led his conquistadores into South America, they found the Incas' artifacts covered with emeralds. No amount of torture could force the Indians to reveal the location of their mines. Only one has ever been discovered. ■ When certain sapphires and rubies are properly cut, a six-pointed star is reflected from minute cavities parallel to the crystal's six sides. This effect is called asterism. Solomon's seal was a star sapphire, and the Ten Commandments are said to have been written on sapphire. Pope Innocent III ordered all his bishops to wear sapphire rings, for sapphire ("beloved of Saturn" in Sanskrit) was believed to preserve its wearer's chastity and to ward off evil. ■

Detail from The Alchemist at Work, *attributed to Pieter Breughel the Elder*

Rubies (from the Latin *ruber*, meaning "red") have long been valued as an aid to their owners' passion. Benvenuto Cellini, an expert on love, set the value of rubies as eight times that of diamonds. ■ Many stones once believed to be rubies are actually spinel, a semi-precious stone generally found near ruby mines. For centuries a famous "ruby" graced the English Crown, later to be unmasked as a spinel. ■ In the Middle Ages, alchemists searched for ways to turn base metals into gold and ordinary stones into gems. But, although they were the scientists of their day, they did not have sufficient knowledge of how nature produces gemstones to produce them in the laboratory. ■ The first man to do so was a French chemist, Moisson, after he developed the electric arc furnace in 1892. Taking his cue from nature, he mixed pure carbon and iron, heated the mixture to 4,000°C. and then plunged it into very cold water. The experiment resulted in a few diamonds of microscopic size. Not until 1904, when another French chemist, Verneuil, produced sapphires and rubies, were precious gems synthesized with real success. Synthetic rubies and sapphires are more nearly

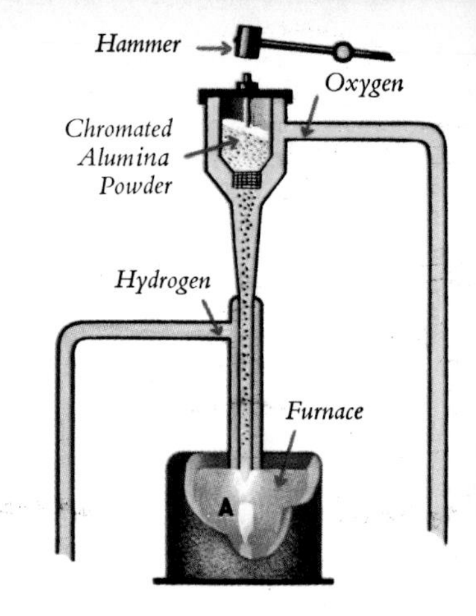

VERNEUIL PROCESS: *Hammer taps alumina powder through a fine screen. Intense flame of hydrogen and oxygen fuses powder to a support (A). Synthetic pear-shaped mass, called "boule", grows as proc-*

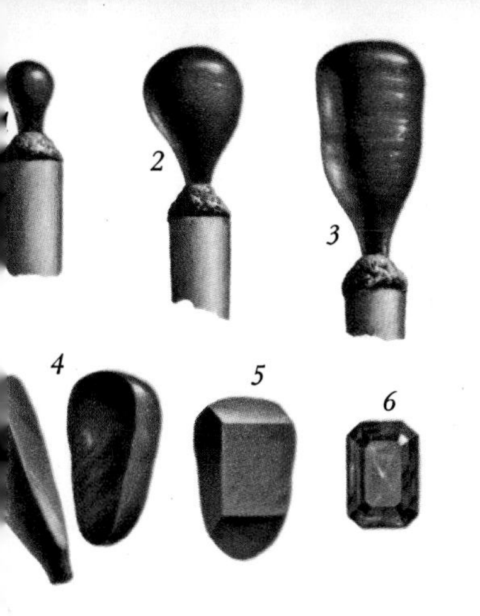

ess repeats. Small amounts of impurities produce the desired colours. Successive stages in the growth of a synthetic ruby (1, 2, 3). Boule is cut in two (4). First facets are cut (5). Finished synthetic gem (6)

perfect than nature's gemstones. But they lack rarity, and so are not considered precious gems. ■ Today synthetic stones of almost every variety—both precious and semi-precious—have been produced. The most recent of them are man-made diamonds of industrial, though not gem, quality. ■ Synthetic stones have had little effect on the price of natural gems, for a professional jeweller can always distinguish between the two. ■ There were, of course, imitation gems long before there were true synthetic stones. The Egyptians did a thriving business with excellent imitations made of coloured glass. In the 18th century a German glassmaker named Strasser developed a highly refractive glass known as *strass* or "paste". Backed with quicksilver and skilfully coloured, paste gems were often passed off as the real thing by unscrupulous salesmen. Properly represented, they are perfectly legitimate, but in time they lose their brilliance. Paste stones are comparatively soft and, unlike true gemstones, can be scratched easily. ■ The distinction between precious and semi-precious stones is often very slight, usually involving rarity or hardness. Fine semi-precious stones are

more valuable than inferior precious ones. Among the most prized of the semi-precious gems is the opal (*upala* is Sanskrit for "precious stone"). Opal begins as a jelly-like silica deposited by hot springs in crevices. As it hardens, much of the water is lost, forming a network of fine cracks. These cracks reflect the light in a play of colours, called opalescence. Stones with the finest cracks have the best play and are known as precious opals (not to be confused with the term as applied to the four precious gems). These opals are rare and costly. ■ At various times throughout history, opals have been believed to be harbingers of bad luck. Queen Victoria restored them to popularity by making them her favourite in order to help

FROM TOP TO BOTTOM: *two "precious" opal pins; Australian black opal in natural state; box inlaid with opal; two Mexican fire opals; a carved white opal mouse, created by Fabergé, famous jeweller to Czar Nicholas II*

Australia's mines, today the world's leading supplier of precious opals. Chrysoberyl is a mineral which is sometimes classed as a precious gem. Surpassed in hardness only by diamond and corundum, it boasts two rare and unusual gemstones in its family: oriental cat's eye and alexandrite. Cut cabochon, cat's eye reveals a single line of silklike sheen, a phenomenon akin to asterism in rubies and sapphires. Alexandrite, named after Czar Alexander II, has the remarkable capacity for appearing green in daylight and red in artificial light. Red and green were the imperial colours of Russia, and the stone's rise to fame was immediate. ■ In ancient times garnets were considered talismen against lightning. In an attempt to enhance their value, red pyrope garnets are sometimes sold under such euphemistic names as *Cape ruby* and *Arizona ruby*. ■ Peridot and kunzite possess colours unique in the gem world, but peridot is softer than quartz and its use as jewellery is quite limited. The finest kunzite is found in California, and good specimens may command high prices. ■ Spinel comes in a wide range of colours, but the faceted red spinels, often called spinel rubies, are the most

Alexandrite when cut (top) is green in daylight and red in artificial light. Below are alexandrite in matrix and oriental cat's eye

Demantoid garnet

Red garnet
in matrix

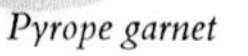

Pyrope garnet

Peridot

Kunzite

These stones are all semi-precious. The long popularity of garnets is attested to by the ring, which is from the Hellenistic period, around 200 B.C. Garnets come in a variety of colours, and orange, yellow, and purple garnets are not uncommon. Topaz is generally seen in the shade shown here, but pale blue and green topaz is found in Russia, and a rare reddish kind in Brazil. Of all gemstones, tourmaline possesses the widest range of colours. The cross-section of the crystal explains the name "watermelon tourmaline"

Topaz

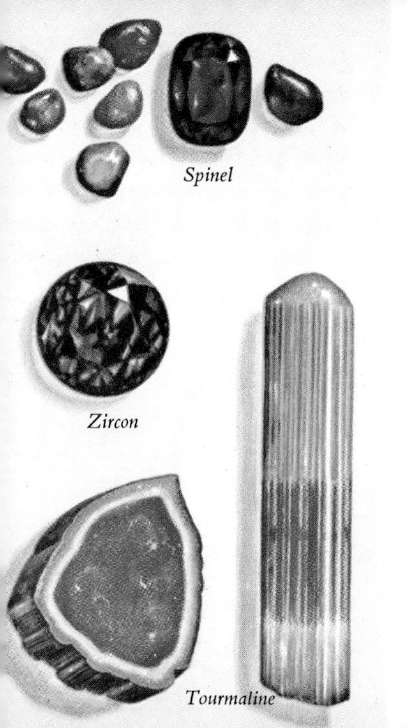
Spinel
Zircon
Tourmaline

in demand. ■ The popularity of zircon is attributable to its ability to refract light with a brilliance second only to diamond. Zircons are found in yellows, greens, and reddish brown. Ironically, the most popular shade of all, blue, is not produced by nature. Blue is artificially induced by heat in a charcoal oven. ■ Topaz, like spinel, is harder than one of the precious gemstones, emerald. Both are suitable for all forms of jewellery because of their hardness. The gem mineral tourmaline is found in the Urals, in Brazil, and in the United States. ■ Quartz is the most widely distributed gemstone on earth. Some varieties, like rock crystal and amethyst, have been considered gems from earliest times. Pliny wrote that "the best cautery for the human body is a ball of crystal, acted on by the sun". A large, clear, crystal ball may command £7,000. ■ Cut like diamonds, rock crystal is marketed under such trade names as "rhinestone" and "Herkimer diamond". ■ Because it can produce electrical charges under pressure, rock crystal is in great demand commercially. Cut into thin wafers, it is used for frequency control in radio equipment. ■ Some of the many faces of

1
2
3
4
5
6
7
8
9
10

the common mineral quartz are shown here. The apple-green stone (1) is chrysoprase. The Chinese snuff bottle (2) is a conglomerate of quartz pebbles known as puddingstone. Natural colouring agents turn quartz crystals into many gems: the yellow citrine (3), the purple amethyst (9), and rose quartz (7). Agate (5) is found in an infinite number of patterns. The parellel lines identify this as banded agate, also used in the earrings from ancient Greece (8). Eye agates (4) are objects of superstition because of their disconcerting appearance. The seaweed effect of moss agate (6) is caused by a mineral, not a plant, inclusion. Rock crystal (10) is a water-clear quartz. The 16th-century cameo (11) was carved from a single agate stone of five layers, each a different colour. A two-layered wafer, similar to these of onyx and sardonyx (13), was used for the Roman cameo (12). ■ Some of the opaque and ornamental gems of the world are depicted here. Coral (1), like the pearl, is an organic gem from the sea. It is composed mostly of calcium carbonate and is a secretion of minute organisms known as coral polyps. The gem varieties, pink to red in colour, come mainly from Mediterranean waters. It is much used for carvings and beads. ■ Jade (2) includes two varieties, nephrite and jadeite. To the Chinese, jade is the precious stone, and the word *yu* means both "jade" and "precious stone". In ancient China, only the first wife could wear jade. The second had to content herself with diamonds. The tiny bottle and its chains are carved from a single piece of jade. ■ In Czarist Russia, carved eggstones were exchanged at Easter. Rhodonite (3), tawny aventurine enclosing another egg of amethyst (4), and lapis lazuli (5) were some of the decorative gems used. Malachite box (6) is fashioned from stone native to the Ural Mountains. Snow flake obsidian (7) is volcanic glass. Turquoise (8), one of the oldest known gems, is found in Asia and the southwestern United States. Opalized wood (9) is used as decorative stone. Orbicular jasper, fashioned into handle of penknife (10), and moonstone (11) complete this display. ■

3
4
5
6
7
8
9
10
11

The decorative use of amber, coral, and pearl goes back to ancient times and has earned them a place among semi-precious gems. Pearl is the most important of this group. ■ Legend tells us that Cleopatra offered to wager Marc Antony that she could consume a meal worth 10,000,000 *sesterces* (about £9,000). When Antony accepted, she took off her pearl pendant, dissolved it in vinegar, and drank it. Actually it would take a long time to dissolve pearls in the acid of vinegar unless they had been pulverized first. But the story points out a difference between pearls and other gems—and a moral. The difference is that pearls are organic in origin and not inorganic minerals. And the moral is that if you own any pearls, never dip them in acid. ■ Superstition has it that a pearl loses its lustre when the owner dies. Since skin moisture keeps the pearl from drying out, the idea is well founded. Pearls are comparatively soft and will become scratched if handled carelessly. Damaged pearls may sometimes be restored by peeling away a layer of the gem's "skin", but this is not always successful. ■ Any mollusc is capable of producing a pearl, for it is made of the same material as the mollusc's shell. But precious pearls come only from molluscs whose shells are formed of mother-of-pearl—hence the name. A pearl is formed when a grain of sand or a tiny parasite enters a mollusc, causing an

The world of pearls, life size, on an oyster shell. The smallest are seed pearls. The long ones are called petals; the pink pearl is pear-shaped. Those in other irregular shapes, like the one used for the body of the Italian Renaissance jewelled cock, are called baroque. The gold earring, with pearls surrounding an emerald, was found in the ruins of Pompeii. Old Greek pin is capped with fresh-water pearl. Pearls come in every shade, but greenish-black is the most valued coloured pearl

irritation. The sea animal encases the intruder in a substance called nacre—successive layers of carbonate of lime and mother-of-pearl. ■ For centuries men have attempted to cultivate pearls commercially by introducing artificial irritants into oysters. In 1913 the secret was discovered: living cell material must accompany the irritant. Today, Japanese pearl farmers enclose a nucleus of mother-of-pearl in a tiny sac cut from the mantle of an oyster. It is seeded in another oyster, which is returned to the water in a cage. Several years must pass before the cultured pearl grows to commercial size. Good cultured pearls can be identified only by X-ray analysis, which reveals the artificial inner core. ■ If pearls are constricted by the muscles of the oyster during their growth, they assume irregular shapes—pear, button, and baroque. ■ The pearl is one of the oldest gems known. The Bible, the Koran, and the Talmud all mention it. The Hindus say that Vishnu created it. The Chinese believed that pearls were really the brains of a dragon. ■ Although pearls are found in many colours, including a rich black, the most precious of all is the silvery-white Oriental pearl. Beauty and value are determined by lustre, iridescence, translucence and, not least, by size. Pearls have always been a favoured ornament of the rich and noble. Portraits of the lords and ladies of the Renaissance reveal the esteem in which pearls were held. When Mary, Queen of Scots, was beheaded, her famous pearls joined the already fabulous collection of her cousin, Elizabeth I. Such was Elizabeth's love of this gem that, even in her hour of death, she was adorned with the most splendid of her pearls. ■ Throughout his-

The so-called Armada portrait of Queen Elizabeth, attributed to Marc Gheeraerts, shows the monarch adorned with pearls in great profusion and variety

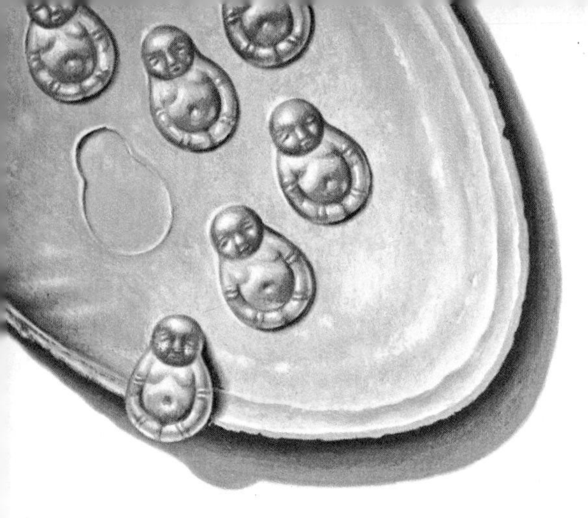

As early as the thirteenth century, the Chinese experimented with artificial pearl culture. Tiny lead figures of Buddha were placed on the inside of the mollusc's shell. In its natural growth process, the animal deposited layers of nacre over the figures

tory, gems have been treasured—first for the powers attributed to them to ward off evil and heal sickness, then for their beauty and intrinsic value. Uncommonly durable, they have been passed on from generation to generation, so that today gems, centuries old, may lie in a jeweller's display case beside newly cut stones. Easily portable and negotiable, they have enabled men to carry a fortune in a pocket from one country to another in times of upheaval. No class of society is immune to their lure; they are alike the badge of solid respectability and the baubles of the underworld. Even in a rapidly changing world, it seems safe to say that, as talismen, as love tokens, as status symbols, as ornaments of surpassing beauty, as examples of craftsmanship, as investments, as indispensable tools of industry, they will be treasured in the future no less than they have been in the past.

INDEX

Figures in **bold type** represent the Mohs Scale of hardness of the gemstones.

GARNET: *Symbol of virtue. Talmudic legend says huge garnet provided only light in Noah's ark. Green dematoid variety is the most valuable*

AMETHYST: *A variety of quartz popular with ancient Greeks and Romans. Originally believed to cure drunkenness; later, symbol of serenity*

AQUAMARINE: *Semi-precious stone, once worn for protection in battle and law courts.* BLOODSTONE: *Worn by men, often carved and initialled*

RUBY: *Second only to diamond in hardness. Found in the hot countries of Siam, Ceylon, Burma; associated with warmth and ardour*

PERIDOT: *Symbol of persuasiveness; a charm against evils of night.* SARDONYX: *Popular as a cameo; thought to ward off melancholy*

SAPPHIRE: *Like the ruby, second to diamond in hardness. Worn by kings to ward off harm; an antidote to poison; considered a sacred gem*